This special book belongs to

_____

The
Cat Album
A Pet Owner's Memory Book

Written and Illustrated by Carol Endler Sterbenz
With Prints From Ernest Nister

Philomel Books

New York

We found you _____

_____

_____

_____

We chose you because _____

_____

_____

_____

Our first thought was _____

_____

_____

_____

Naming You

Some famous cats:

Cheshire Cat, Puss-in-Boots, Nelson, Knurremuree, Muessa, Kiki, Felix, Greymalkin, All Ball, Tobermory, Snowbell, Dick Whittington's Cat, Mephisto, Mistoffelees, Griddlebone, Macavity, Lucifer, Mittens, Pasht, Morris, Zoroaster, Widget, Slippers, Selina, Blatherskite, Grizabella, Pudlenka, Old Deuteronomy, Mungojerrie, Rumpleteazer, Garfield, Heathcliff, Bastet.

Some Suggestions:

Ming, Minou, Drusilla, Cecily, Maxine, Whiskers, Tiger Lily, Tabitha, Gwyneth, Cleo, Sylvester, Midnight, Pumpkin, Pie Wacket, Cornelia, Clouseau, Jezebel, Hattie, Twenty-Eight, Victoria, Maneki-Neko, Camellia.

We thought of these names for you: _____

_____

_____

_____

After we held you and watched you, we chose

You arrived on _____ , the ____ day of _____ ,

19 ____ , at ____ o'clock in _____ .
(town)

You weighed ____ and were ____ long.

Your eyes were closed at first,

but when you opened them, they were _____ .

Your special markings were _____

_____ .

And your fur was _____ .

You had ____ brothers

and ____ sisters.

Paw Print

Photograph

Official Adoption Certificate

This is to certify

that _____ , who was born
(name of cat)

on the ___ day of _____ , 19 ___ ,

in the town of _____

has been adopted by _____ ,

who resides at _____

and who has promised continual

loving care and affection.

Officially signed and noted

this ___ day of _____ , 19 ___ .

(Signature)

Caring for You

When you were ＿＿ weeks of age,

we brought you to see Dr. ＿＿＿＿＿＿＿＿＿＿＿＿ , your veterinarian.

He lives at ＿＿＿＿＿＿＿＿＿＿＿＿＿＿＿＿＿＿＿＿

His telephone number is ＿＿＿＿＿＿＿＿＿＿＿＿＿＿

And in emergency ＿＿＿＿＿＿＿＿＿＿＿＿＿＿＿＿

His comments: ＿＿＿＿＿＿＿＿＿＿＿＿＿＿＿＿＿

＿＿＿＿＿＿＿＿＿＿＿＿＿＿＿＿＿＿＿＿＿＿＿＿＿

＿＿＿＿＿＿＿＿＿＿＿＿＿＿＿＿＿＿＿＿＿＿＿＿＿

Other Important Visits ＿＿＿＿＿＿＿＿＿＿＿＿＿＿

＿＿＿＿＿＿＿＿＿＿＿＿＿＿＿＿＿＿＿＿＿＿＿＿＿

＿＿＿＿＿＿＿＿＿＿＿＿＿＿＿＿＿＿＿＿＿＿＿＿＿

＿＿＿＿＿＿＿＿＿＿＿＿＿＿＿＿＿＿＿＿＿＿＿＿＿

＿＿＿＿＿＿＿＿＿＿＿＿＿＿＿＿＿＿＿＿＿＿＿＿＿

Vaccination Schedule

Vaccine	Age to Begin
Distemper FPL (Feline panleukopenia)	8 weeks: 2 boosters, 4 weeks apart. Annual booster vaccinations thereafter.
Feline Viral Rhinotracheitis (FVR)	12 weeks: 2 boosters, 4 weeks apart. Annual booster vaccinations thereafter.
Feline Calicivirus (FCV)	12 weeks. Annual booster vaccinations thereafter.
Feline Leukemia Virus (FcLV)	9 weeks or older.* Rebooster at 3 weeks and 3 months. Annual booster vaccinations thereafter. *Cat should be FcLV tested before or at time of first vaccination.
Feline Chlamydia (Pneumonitus)	Optional; 10–12 weeks. Annual booster vaccinations thereafter.
Rabies (Killed virus vaccine)	6 months. Annual booster vaccinations thereafter.

Be sure to consult your veterinarian for an immunization program for your cat.

When You Are Not Feeling Well

Date	Illness

Comments

Date   Weight

Comments

The Family of Cats

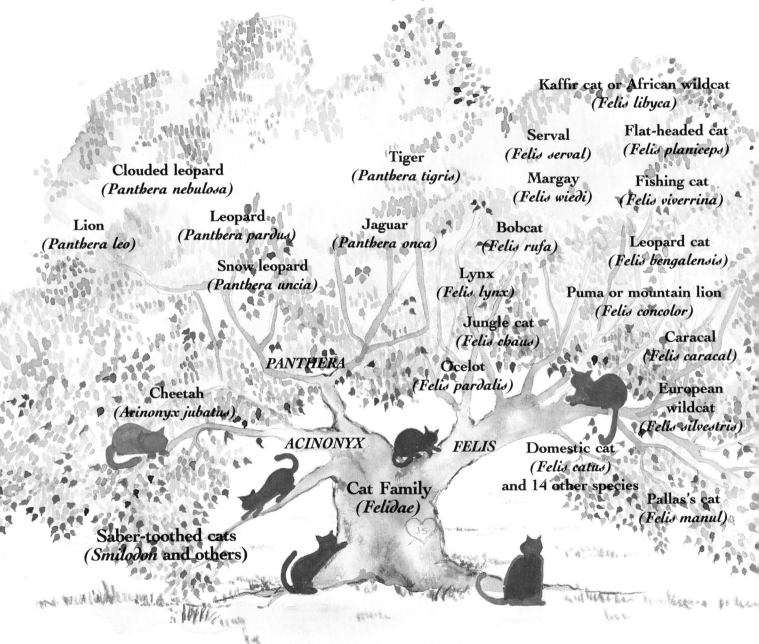

Kaffir cat or African wildcat
(*Felis libyca*)

Serval
(*Felis serval*)

Flat-headed cat
(*Felis planiceps*)

Clouded leopard
(*Panthera nebulosa*)

Tiger
(*Panthera tigris*)

Margay
(*Felis wiedi*)

Fishing cat
(*Felis viverrina*)

Lion
(*Panthera leo*)

Leopard
(*Panthera pardus*)

Jaguar
(*Panthera onca*)

Bobcat
(*Felis rufa*)

Leopard cat
(*Felis bengalensis*)

Snow leopard
(*Panthera uncia*)

Lynx
(*Felis lynx*)

Puma or mountain lion
(*Felis concolor*)

PANTHERA

Jungle cat
(*Felis chaus*)

Caracal
(*Felis caracal*)

Cheetah
(*Acinonyx jubatus*)

Ocelot
(*Felis pardalis*)

ACINONYX

FELIS

European
wildcat
(*Felis silvestris*)

Domestic cat
(*Felis catus*)
and 14 other species

Cat Family
(*Felidae*)

Pallas's cat
(*Felis manul*)

Saber-toothed cats
(*Smilodon* and others)

Carnivores

The Cats in Our Family

A Few Thoughts to Share

Photograph

Photograph

Your Family

Photograph

Photograph

Some Special Days With You

All About You

Where you nap _____

_____

_____

Your favorite games _____

_____

Your favorite hiding places _____

_____

_____

What you eat _____

_____

And as a treat, you have _____

_____

_____

The affectionate things you do _____

_____

_____

The naughty things you do _____

_____

_____

The funny things you do _____

_____

_____

You understand these words _____

_____

_____

We trained you to _____

_____

_____

More About You

You are curious about _____
_____
_____

You get angry when _____
_____
_____

You seem jealous of _____
_____
_____

You dislike _____
_____
_____

You seem most content when _____
_____
_____
_____

Away From Home

Places you have visited _____
_____

When we go away, you are cared for by _____ ,
whose address is _____
and whose telephone number is _____ .
Special instructions from me: _____
_____
_____
_____

_____

_____

_____